CW00419092

Z Z
Z

THIS BOOK
WILL MAKE YOU
FALL ASLEEP

summersdale

THIS BOOK WILL MAKE YOU FALL ASLEEP

An Hachette UK Company
www.hachette.co.uk

Summersdale Publishers Ltd
Part of Octopus Publishing Group Limited
Carmelite House
50 Victoria Embankment
LONDON
EC4Y 0DZ
UK

www.summersdale.com

Printed and bound in China

ISBN: 978-1-78685-997-6

Substantial discounts on bulk quantities of Summersdale books are available to corporations, professional associations and other organizations. For details contact general enquiries: telephone: +44 (0) 1243 771107 or email: enquiries@summersdale.com.

To.................................

From................................

INTRODUCTION

Are you tired of sleepless nights? Do you wish you could drop off in two shakes of lamb's tail? Then say hello to Kip!

Follow your new woolly friend through this book. Complete the puzzles and count the sheep when they appear, feel your eyes grow heavier with each turn of the page, and allow Kip to guide you through to the Land of Nod. You will be snoozing in no time!

Find answers to the puzzles on pp.158-9

Think in the morning.
Act in the noon.
Eat in the evening.
Sleep in the night.

WILLIAM BLAKE

GUIDE KIP
TO THE PILLOW

There is a time for
many words and there is
a time for sleep.

HOMER

GUIDE KIP TO THE PILLOW

Make your bedroom a sanctuary so that you'll look forward to bedtime. Keep it clean and tidy, use soft lighting, and only have pictures and trinkets that bring you joy.

Happiness is waking up, looking at the clock and finding that you still have two hours left to sleep.

CHARLES M. SCHULZ

COMPLETE THE WORD SEARCH

Dream

Doze

Nap

Rest

Snooze

t	p	c	a	d	r	n	i
e	d	r	e	a	m	p	q
c	o	n	x	m	u	a	k
e	z	o	o	n	s	p	y
f	e	t	p	j	l	w	n
a	w	q	s	m	o	r	p
r	l	n	c	e	t	x	a
o	v	e	p	w	r	m	n

SWITCH OFF YOUR GADGETS
AT LEAST HALF AN HOUR
BEFORE BEDTIME TO ALLOW
YOUR MIND TO WIND
DOWN AND PREPARE
ITSELF FOR SLEEP.

I'm trying to read
a book on how to relax,
but I keep falling asleep.

JAMES M. LOY

Spot the five differences

Guide Kip to the pillow

WRITE A JOURNAL BEFORE YOU GO TO SLEEP. GETTING YOUR WORRIES OUT OF YOUR HEAD AND ONTO PAPER CAN HELP TO CLEAR YOUR MIND AND MAKE YOU FEEL CALM.

It is a common experience that a problem difficult at night is resolved in the morning after the committee of sleep has worked on it.

JOHN STEINBECK

FIND THE SLEEPING SHEEP

The amount of sleep required by the average person is five minutes more.

WILSON MIZNER

Find the pair

Have gentle lighting in your bedroom to help ease the transition from day to night. The softer light will help signal to your body that it's time to sleep.

FIND THE PAIR

Guide Kip to the pillow

Life is something
to do when you
can't get to sleep.

FRAN LEBOWITZ

ENJOY A HOT DRINK
BEFORE YOU GO TO BED,
SUCH AS A FRUIT TEA,
HERBAL TEA, OR A CUP
OF WARM MILK, TO
SOOTHE YOU INTO SLEEP.

Sleeping is no mean art:
for its sake one must
stay awake all day.

FRIEDRICH NIETZSCHE

Guide Kip to the pillow

O sleep
O gentle sleep
Nature's soft nurse.

WILLIAM SHAKESPEARE

Guide Kip to the pillow

A good laugh
and a long sleep
are the two best cures
for anything.

IRISH PROVERB

Spot the five differences

There is no sunrise
so beautiful that it is
worth waking me
up to see it.

MINDY KALING

Find "calm"

m	c	a	c	a	m	a	c
c	m	a	m	l	c	a	c
a	l	m	l	c	m	m	a
l	a	c	a	l	a	l	m
a	m	a	m	c	l	a	l
m	l	a	l	m	a	c	c
l	a	l	m	l	m	a	l
a	m	c	a	c	a	m	a

A well-spent day
brings happy sleep.

LEONARDO DA VINCI

GUIDE KIP TO THE PILLOW

FIND THE PILLOW

The best eraser
in the world is a
good night's sleep.

ORLANDO ALOYSIUS BATTISTA

A soothing bath is a wonderful way to relax your mind and body before bed. Add your favourite bubbles or essential oils to make it extra special.

O bed! O bed!
delicious bed!

That heaven upon earth
to the weary head.

THOMAS HOOD

Help Kip to catch some Zzzs

Take a nap in a fireplace and you'll sleep like a log.

ELLEN DeGENERES

GUIDE KIP TO THE PILLOW

Sit anywhere you feel comfortable and close your eyes. Breathe in slowly through your nose until your lungs are full. Hold for four slow counts, then exhale slowly. Repeat until you are feeling calm.

My mother told me
to follow my dreams,
so I took a nap.

ANONYMOUS

FIND THE PAIR

I count it as a certainty that, in paradise, everyone naps.

TOM HODGKINSON

Complete the word search

Bedtime

Sleep

Shut-eye

Relax

Slumber

Forty winks

s	k	n	i	w	y	t	r	o	f	p	t
l	k	j	h	g	f	d	s	e	t	r	s
p	o	u	y	u	t	s	l	e	e	p	l
a	e	n	h	u	r	h	v	q	t	s	a
t	f	m	o	f	c	u	x	s	s	q	v
m	w	e	i	r	u	t	k	n	l	m	c
h	f	l	n	t	f	e	g	y	u	p	z
q	u	f	v	c	d	y	e	w	m	a	s
l	t	r	e	s	x	e	u	q	b	z	w
p	q	y	r	d	v	b	b	o	e	j	u
r	e	l	a	x	q	k	s	n	r	o	p
c	h	v	e	w	i	h	v	l	m	u	x

No day is so bad
it can't be fixed
with a nap.

CARRIE SNOW

Spot the five differences

SWEET DREAMS

ANSWERS

pp.12–13

pp.36–37

pp.56–57

pp.18–19

pp.42–43

pp.64–65

pp.28–29

pp.50–51

pp.68–69

pp.80–81

pp.108–109

pp.130–131

pp.88–89

pp.112–113

pp.138–139

pp.94–95

pp.122–123

pp.144–145

s	k	n	i	w	y	t	r	o	f	p	t
l	k	j	h	g	f	d	s	e	t	r	s
p	o	u	y	u	t	s	l	e	e	p	l
a	e	n	h	u	r	h	v	q	t	s	a
t	f	m	o	f	c	u	x	s	s	q	v
m	w	e	i	r	u	t	k	n	l	m	c
h	f	l	n	t	f	e	g	y	u	p	z
q	u	f	v	c	d	y	e	w	m	a	s
l	t	r	e	s	x	e	u	q	b	z	w
p	q	y	r	d	v	b	b	o	e	j	u
r	e	l	a	x	q	k	s	n	r	o	p
c	h	v	e	w	i	h	v	l	m	u	x

pp.102–103

m	c	a	c	a	m	a	c
c	m	a	m	l	c	a	c
a	l	m	l	c	m	m	a
l	a	c	a	l	a	l	m
a	m	a	m	c	l	a	l
m	l	a	l	m	a	c	c
l	a	l	m	l	m	a	l
a	m	c	a	c	a	m	a

pp.150–151

If you're interested in finding out more about our books, find us on Facebook at Summersdale Publishers and follow us on Twitter at @summersdale.

www.summersdale.com

IMAGE CREDITS